MOTHER'S
LITTLE HELPER

TODAY'S DATE

/   /

TODAY'S STRESS LEVEL

1   2   3   4   5   11

	STUFF TO DO FOR EVERYONE ELSE	✓	ITEMS TO BUY FOR EVERYONE ELSE	✓
01				
02				
03				
04				
05				
06				
07				
08				
09				
10				
11				
12				
13				
14				

JOBS I MUST PERFORM FOR EVERYONE ELSE TODAY

☐ HOUSEKEEPER   ☐ ALARM CLOCK   ☐ HUMAN HANKY
☐ COMPLAINT DEPARTMENT   ☐ TUSHY WIPER   ☐ MEDIATOR
☐ SOCK FINDER   ☐ DOCTOR   ☐ ATM
☐ THERAPIST   ☐ CHEF   ☐ COACH
☐ CHAUFFEUR   ☐ GOOD COP   ☐ TOOTH FAIRY
☐ BOOBOO KISSER   ☐ BAD COP   ☐ ....
☐ HOMEWORK TUTOR   ☐ STORYTELLER   ☐ ALL OF THE ABOVE

ONE THING I COULD POSSIBLY DO FOR MYS[...]

01	

D0275577

"REMEMBER, MOTHER KNOWS BES[...]

MOTHER'S
LITTLE HELPER

TODAY'S DATE

/ /

TODAY'S STRESS LEVEL

1   2   3   4   5   11

	STUFF TO DO FOR EVERYONE ELSE	✓	ITEMS TO BUY FOR EVERYONE ELSE	✓
01				
02				
03				
04				
05				
06				
07				
08				
09				
10				
11				
12				
13				
14				

JOBS I MUST PERFORM FOR EVERYONE ELSE TODAY

☐ HOUSEKEEPER
☐ COMPLAINT DEPARTMENT
☐ SOCK FINDER
☐ THERAPIST
☐ CHAUFFEUR
☐ BOOBOO KISSER
☐ HOMEWORK TUTOR

☐ ALARM CLOCK
☐ TUSHY WIPER
☐ DOCTOR
☐ CHEF
☐ GOOD COP
☐ BAD COP
☐ STORYTELLER

☐ HUMAN HANKY
☐ MEDIATOR
☐ ATM
☐ COACH
☐ TOOTH FAIRY
☐ ....
☐ ALL OF THE ABOVE

ONE THING I COULD POSSIBLY DO FOR MYSELF TODAY	✓
01	

"REMEMBER, MOTHER KNOWS BEST"

MOTHER'S LITTLE HELPER

KNOCKKNOCKSTUFF.COM ■ © 2018 KNOCK KNOCK LLC

TODAY'S DATE

/ /

TODAY'S STRESS LEVEL

1 2 3 4 5 11

	STUFF TO DO FOR EVERYONE ELSE	✓	ITEMS TO BUY FOR EVERYONE ELSE	✓
01				
02				
03				
04				
05				
06				
07				
08				
09				
10				
11				
12				
13				
14				

JOBS I MUST PERFORM FOR EVERYONE ELSE TODAY

☐ HOUSEKEEPER   ☐ ALARM CLOCK   ☐ HUMAN HANKY

☐ COMPLAINT DEPARTMENT   ☐ TUSHY WIPER   ☐ MEDIATOR

☐ SOCK FINDER   ☐ DOCTOR   ☐ ATM

☐ THERAPIST   ☐ CHEF   ☐ COACH

☐ CHAUFFEUR   ☐ GOOD COP   ☐ TOOTH FAIRY

☐ BOOBOO KISSER   ☐ BAD COP   ☐ ....

☐ HOMEWORK TUTOR   ☐ STORYTELLER   ☐ ALL OF THE ABOVE

	ONE THING I COULD POSSIBLY DO FOR MYSELF TODAY	✓
01		

"REMEMBER, MOTHER KNOWS BEST"

MOTHER'S
LITTLE HELPER

TODAY'S DATE
/ /

TODAY'S STRESS LEVEL

1 2 3 4 5 11

STUFF TO DO FOR EVERYONE ELSE	✓	ITEMS TO BUY FOR EVERYONE ELSE	✓
01			
02			
03			
04			
05			
06			
07			
08			
09			
10			
11			
12			
13			
14			

JOBS I MUST PERFORM FOR EVERYONE ELSE TODAY

- ☐ HOUSEKEEPER
- ☐ COMPLAINT DEPARTMENT
- ☐ SOCK FINDER
- ☐ THERAPIST
- ☐ CHAUFFEUR
- ☐ BOOBOO KISSER
- ☐ HOMEWORK TUTOR
- ☐ ALARM CLOCK
- ☐ TUSHY WIPER
- ☐ DOCTOR
- ☐ CHEF
- ☐ GOOD COP
- ☐ BAD COP
- ☐ STORYTELLER
- ☐ HUMAN HANKY
- ☐ MEDIATOR
- ☐ ATM
- ☐ COACH
- ☐ TOOTH FAIRY
- ☐ ....
- ☐ ALL OF THE ABOVE

ONE THING I COULD POSSIBLY DO FOR MYSELF TODAY	✓
01	

"REMEMBER, MOTHER KNOWS BEST"

KNOCKKNOCKSTUFF.COM ▪ © 2018 KNOCK KNOCK LLC

MOTHER'S LITTLE HELPER

TODAY'S DATE

/ /

TODAY'S STRESS LEVEL

1 2 3 4 5 11

	STUFF TO DO FOR EVERYONE ELSE	✓	ITEMS TO BUY FOR EVERYONE ELSE	✓
01				
02				
03				
04				
05				
06				
07				
08				
09				
10				
11				
12				
13				
14				

JOBS I MUST PERFORM FOR EVERYONE ELSE TODAY

☐ HOUSEKEEPER	☐ ALARM CLOCK	☐ HUMAN HANKY
☐ COMPLAINT DEPARTMENT	☐ TUSHY WIPER	☐ MEDIATOR
☐ SOCK FINDER	☐ DOCTOR	☐ ATM
☐ THERAPIST	☐ CHEF	☐ COACH
☐ CHAUFFEUR	☐ GOOD COP	☐ TOOTH FAIRY
☐ BOOBOO KISSER	☐ BAD COP	☐ ....
☐ HOMEWORK TUTOR	☐ STORYTELLER	☐ ALL OF THE ABOVE

ONE THING I COULD POSSIBLY DO FOR MYSELF TODAY ✓

01	

"REMEMBER, MOTHER KNOWS BEST"

MOTHER'S LITTLE HELPER

TODAY'S STRESS LEVEL

1   2   3   4   5   11

	STUFF TO DO FOR EVERYONE ELSE	✓	ITEMS TO BUY FOR EVERYONE ELSE	✓
01				
02				
03				
04				
05				
06				
07				
08				
09				
10				
11				
12				
13				
14				

JOBS I MUST PERFORM FOR EVERYONE ELSE TODAY

- ☐ HOUSEKEEPER
- ☐ COMPLAINT DEPARTMENT
- ☐ SOCK FINDER
- ☐ THERAPIST
- ☐ CHAUFFEUR
- ☐ BOOBOO KISSER
- ☐ HOMEWORK TUTOR

- ☐ ALARM CLOCK
- ☐ TUSHY WIPER
- ☐ DOCTOR
- ☐ CHEF
- ☐ GOOD COP
- ☐ BAD COP
- ☐ STORYTELLER

- ☐ HUMAN HANKY
- ☐ MEDIATOR
- ☐ ATM
- ☐ COACH
- ☐ TOOTH FAIRY
- ☐ ....
- ☐ ALL OF THE ABOVE

	ONE THING I COULD POSSIBLY DO FOR MYSELF TODAY	✓
01		

"REMEMBER, MOTHER KNOWS BEST"

MOTHER'S LITTLE HELPER

	STUFF TO DO FOR EVERYONE ELSE	✓	ITEMS TO BUY FOR EVERYONE ELSE	✓
01				
02				
03				
04				
05				
06				
07				
08				
09				
10				
11				
12				
13				
14				

JOBS I MUST PERFORM FOR EVERYONE ELSE TODAY

- ☐ HOUSEKEEPER
- ☐ COMPLAINT DEPARTMENT
- ☐ SOCK FINDER
- ☐ THERAPIST
- ☐ CHAUFFEUR
- ☐ BOOBOO KISSER
- ☐ HOMEWORK TUTOR

- ☐ ALARM CLOCK
- ☐ TUSHY WIPER
- ☐ DOCTOR
- ☐ CHEF
- ☐ GOOD COP
- ☐ BAD COP
- ☐ STORYTELLER

- ☐ HUMAN HANKY
- ☐ MEDIATOR
- ☐ ATM
- ☐ COACH
- ☐ TOOTH FAIRY
- ☐ ....
- ☐ ALL OF THE ABOVE

ONE THING I COULD POSSIBLY DO FOR MYSELF TODAY	✓
01	

"REMEMBER, MOTHER KNOWS BEST"

MOTHER'S LITTLE HELPER

TODAY'S DATE
/ /

TODAY'S STRESS LEVEL
1 2 3 4 5 11

	STUFF TO DO FOR EVERYONE ELSE	✓	ITEMS TO BUY FOR EVERYONE ELSE	✓
01				
02				
03				
04				
05				
06				
07				
08				
09				
10				
11				
12				
13				
14				

JOBS I MUST PERFORM FOR EVERYONE ELSE TODAY

- ☐ HOUSEKEEPER
- ☐ COMPLAINT DEPARTMENT
- ☐ SOCK FINDER
- ☐ THERAPIST
- ☐ CHAUFFEUR
- ☐ BOOBOO KISSER
- ☐ HOMEWORK TUTOR

- ☐ ALARM CLOCK
- ☐ TUSHY WIPER
- ☐ DOCTOR
- ☐ CHEF
- ☐ GOOD COP
- ☐ BAD COP
- ☐ STORYTELLER

- ☐ HUMAN HANKY
- ☐ MEDIATOR
- ☐ ATM
- ☐ COACH
- ☐ TOOTH FAIRY
- ☐ ....
- ☐ ALL OF THE ABOVE

	ONE THING I COULD POSSIBLY DO FOR MYSELF TODAY	✓
01		

"REMEMBER, MOTHER KNOWS BEST"

MOTHER'S LITTLE HELPER

TODAY'S DATE

/ /

TODAY'S STRESS LEVEL

1   2   3   4   5   11

	STUFF TO DO FOR EVERYONE ELSE	✓	ITEMS TO BUY FOR EVERYONE ELSE	✓
01				
02				
03				
04				
05				
06				
07				
08				
09				
10				
11				
12				
13				
14				

JOBS I MUST PERFORM FOR EVERYONE ELSE TODAY

☐ HOUSEKEEPER   ☐ ALARM CLOCK   ☐ HUMAN HANKY

☐ COMPLAINT DEPARTMENT ☐ TUSHY WIPER   ☐ MEDIATOR

☐ SOCK FINDER   ☐ DOCTOR   ☐ ATM

☐ THERAPIST   ☐ CHEF   ☐ COACH

☐ CHAUFFEUR   ☐ GOOD COP   ☐ TOOTH FAIRY

☐ BOOBOO KISSER   ☐ BAD COP   ☐ ....

☐ HOMEWORK TUTOR   ☐ STORYTELLER   ☐ ALL OF THE ABOVE

ONE THING I COULD POSSIBLY DO FOR MYSELF TODAY	✓
01	

"REMEMBER, MOTHER KNOWS BEST"

MOTHER'S
LITTLE HELPER

TODAY'S DATE

/ /

TODAY'S STRESS LEVEL

1   2   3   4   5   11

	STUFF TO DO FOR EVERYONE ELSE	✓	ITEMS TO BUY FOR EVERYONE ELSE	✓
01				
02				
03				
04				
05				
06				
07				
08				
09				
10				
11				
12				
13				
14				

JOBS I MUST PERFORM FOR EVERYONE ELSE TODAY

- ☐ HOUSEKEEPER
- ☐ COMPLAINT DEPARTMENT
- ☐ SOCK FINDER
- ☐ THERAPIST
- ☐ CHAUFFEUR
- ☐ BOOBOO KISSER
- ☐ HOMEWORK TUTOR

- ☐ ALARM CLOCK
- ☐ TUSHY WIPER
- ☐ DOCTOR
- ☐ CHEF
- ☐ GOOD COP
- ☐ BAD COP
- ☐ STORYTELLER

- ☐ HUMAN HANKY
- ☐ MEDIATOR
- ☐ ATM
- ☐ COACH
- ☐ TOOTH FAIRY
- ☐ ....
- ☐ ALL OF THE ABOVE

	ONE THING I COULD POSSIBLY DO FOR MYSELF TODAY	✓
01		

"REMEMBER, MOTHER KNOWS BEST"

MOTHER'S LITTLE HELPER

TODAY'S DATE

/   /

TODAY'S STRESS LEVEL

1   2   3   4   5   11

	STUFF TO DO FOR EVERYONE ELSE	✓	ITEMS TO BUY FOR EVERYONE ELSE	✓
01				
02				
03				
04				
05				
06				
07				
08				
09				
10				
11				
12				
13				
14				

JOBS I MUST PERFORM FOR EVERYONE ELSE TODAY

- ☐ HOUSEKEEPER
- ☐ COMPLAINT DEPARTMENT
- ☐ SOCK FINDER
- ☐ THERAPIST
- ☐ CHAUFFEUR
- ☐ BOOBOO KISSER
- ☐ HOMEWORK TUTOR
- ☐ ALARM CLOCK
- ☐ TUSHY WIPER
- ☐ DOCTOR
- ☐ CHEF
- ☐ GOOD COP
- ☐ BAD COP
- ☐ STORYTELLER
- ☐ HUMAN HANKY
- ☐ MEDIATOR
- ☐ ATM
- ☐ COACH
- ☐ TOOTH FAIRY
- ☐ ....
- ☐ ALL OF THE ABOVE

ONE THING I COULD POSSIBLY DO FOR MYSELF TODAY   ✓

01	

"REMEMBER, MOTHER KNOWS BEST"

KNOCKKNOCKSTUFF.COM ▪ © 2018 KNOCK KNOCK LLC

MOTHER'S
LITTLE HELPER

TODAY'S DATE

/   /

TODAY'S STRESS LEVEL

1   2   3   4   5   11

	STUFF TO DO FOR EVERYONE ELSE	✓	ITEMS TO BUY FOR EVERYONE ELSE	✓
01				
02				
03				
04				
05				
06				
07				
08				
09				
10				
11				
12				
13				
14				

JOBS I MUST PERFORM FOR EVERYONE ELSE TODAY

☐ HOUSEKEEPER   ☐ ALARM CLOCK   ☐ HUMAN HANKY
☐ COMPLAINT DEPARTMENT   ☐ TUSHY WIPER   ☐ MEDIATOR
☐ SOCK FINDER   ☐ DOCTOR   ☐ ATM
☐ THERAPIST   ☐ CHEF   ☐ COACH
☐ CHAUFFEUR   ☐ GOOD COP   ☐ TOOTH FAIRY
☐ BOOBOO KISSER   ☐ BAD COP   ☐ ....
☐ HOMEWORK TUTOR   ☐ STORYTELLER   ☐ ALL OF THE ABOVE

	ONE THING I COULD POSSIBLY DO FOR MYSELF TODAY	✓
01		

"REMEMBER, MOTHER KNOWS BEST"

MOTHER'S LITTLE HELPER

TODAY'S DATE

/ /

TODAY'S STRESS LEVEL

1   2   3   4   5   11

	STUFF TO DO FOR EVERYONE ELSE	✓	ITEMS TO BUY FOR EVERYONE ELSE	✓
01				
02				
03				
04				
05				
06				
07				
08				
09				
10				
11				
12				
13				
14				

JOBS I MUST PERFORM FOR EVERYONE ELSE TODAY

☐ HOUSEKEEPER	☐ ALARM CLOCK	☐ HUMAN HANKY
☐ COMPLAINT DEPARTMENT	☐ TUSHY WIPER	☐ MEDIATOR
☐ SOCK FINDER	☐ DOCTOR	☐ ATM
☐ THERAPIST	☐ CHEF	☐ COACH
☐ CHAUFFEUR	☐ GOOD COP	☐ TOOTH FAIRY
☐ BOOBOO KISSER	☐ BAD COP	☐ ....
☐ HOMEWORK TUTOR	☐ STORYTELLER	☐ ALL OF THE ABOVE

ONE THING I COULD POSSIBLY DO FOR MYSELF TODAY	✓
01	

"REMEMBER, MOTHER KNOWS BEST"

MOTHER'S LITTLE HELPER

TODAY'S DATE

/ /

TODAY'S STRESS LEVEL

1 2 3 4 5 11

#	STUFF TO DO FOR EVERYONE ELSE	✓	ITEMS TO BUY FOR EVERYONE ELSE	✓
01				
02				
03				
04				
05				
06				
07				
08				
09				
10				
11				
12				
13				
14				

JOBS I MUST PERFORM FOR EVERYONE ELSE TODAY

- ☐ HOUSEKEEPER
- ☐ COMPLAINT DEPARTMENT
- ☐ SOCK FINDER
- ☐ THERAPIST
- ☐ CHAUFFEUR
- ☐ BOOBOO KISSER
- ☐ HOMEWORK TUTOR

- ☐ ALARM CLOCK
- ☐ TUSHY WIPER
- ☐ DOCTOR
- ☐ CHEF
- ☐ GOOD COP
- ☐ BAD COP
- ☐ STORYTELLER

- ☐ HUMAN HANKY
- ☐ MEDIATOR
- ☐ ATM
- ☐ COACH
- ☐ TOOTH FAIRY
- ☐ ....
- ☐ ALL OF THE ABOVE

	ONE THING I COULD POSSIBLY DO FOR MYSELF TODAY	✓
01		

"REMEMBER, MOTHER KNOWS BEST"

MOTHER'S
LITTLE HELPER

TODAY'S DATE

/ /

TODAY'S STRESS LEVEL

1 2 3 4 5 11

	STUFF TO DO FOR EVERYONE ELSE	✓	ITEMS TO BUY FOR EVERYONE ELSE	✓
01				
02				
03				
04				
05				
06				
07				
08				
09				
10				
11				
12				
13				
14				

JOBS I MUST PERFORM FOR EVERYONE ELSE TODAY

☐ HOUSEKEEPER   ☐ ALARM CLOCK   ☐ HUMAN HANKY

☐ COMPLAINT DEPARTMENT   ☐ TUSHY WIPER   ☐ MEDIATOR

☐ SOCK FINDER   ☐ DOCTOR   ☐ ATM

☐ THERAPIST   ☐ CHEF   ☐ COACH

☐ CHAUFFEUR   ☐ GOOD COP   ☐ TOOTH FAIRY

☐ BOOBOO KISSER   ☐ BAD COP   ☐ ....

☐ HOMEWORK TUTOR   ☐ STORYTELLER   ☐ ALL OF THE ABOVE

ONE THING I COULD POSSIBLY DO FOR MYSELF TODAY	✓
01	

"REMEMBER, MOTHER KNOWS BEST"

MOTHER'S LITTLE HELPER

	STUFF TO DO FOR EVERYONE ELSE	✓	ITEMS TO BUY FOR EVERYONE ELSE	✓
01				
02				
03				
04				
05				
06				
07				
08				
09				
10				
11				
12				
13				
14				

JOBS I MUST PERFORM FOR EVERYONE ELSE TODAY

- ☐ HOUSEKEEPER
- ☐ COMPLAINT DEPARTMENT
- ☐ SOCK FINDER
- ☐ THERAPIST
- ☐ CHAUFFEUR
- ☐ BOOBOO KISSER
- ☐ HOMEWORK TUTOR
- ☐ ALARM CLOCK
- ☐ TUSHY WIPER
- ☐ DOCTOR
- ☐ CHEF
- ☐ GOOD COP
- ☐ BAD COP
- ☐ STORYTELLER
- ☐ HUMAN HANKY
- ☐ MEDIATOR
- ☐ ATM
- ☐ COACH
- ☐ TOOTH FAIRY
- ☐ ....
- ☐ ALL OF THE ABOVE

ONE THING I COULD POSSIBLY DO FOR MYSELF TODAY	✓
01	

"REMEMBER, MOTHER KNOWS BEST"

MOTHER'S
LITTLE HELPER

TODAY'S DATE

/ /

TODAY'S STRESS LEVEL

1 2 3 4 5 11

	STUFF TO DO FOR EVERYONE ELSE	✓	ITEMS TO BUY FOR EVERYONE ELSE	✓
01				
02				
03				
04				
05				
06				
07				
08				
09				
10				
11				
12				
13				
14				

JOBS I MUST PERFORM FOR EVERYONE ELSE TODAY

- ☐ HOUSEKEEPER
- ☐ COMPLAINT DEPARTMENT
- ☐ SOCK FINDER
- ☐ THERAPIST
- ☐ CHAUFFEUR
- ☐ BOOBOO KISSER
- ☐ HOMEWORK TUTOR

- ☐ ALARM CLOCK
- ☐ TUSHY WIPER
- ☐ DOCTOR
- ☐ CHEF
- ☐ GOOD COP
- ☐ BAD COP
- ☐ STORYTELLER

- ☐ HUMAN HANKY
- ☐ MEDIATOR
- ☐ ATM
- ☐ COACH
- ☐ TOOTH FAIRY
- ☐ ....
- ☐ ALL OF THE ABOVE

	ONE THING I COULD POSSIBLY DO FOR MYSELF TODAY	✓
01		

"REMEMBER, MOTHER KNOWS BEST"

MOTHER'S
LITTLE HELPER

#	STUFF TO DO FOR EVERYONE ELSE	✓	ITEMS TO BUY FOR EVERYONE ELSE	✓
01				
02				
03				
04				
05				
06				
07				
08				
09				
10				
11				
12				
13				
14				

JOBS I MUST PERFORM FOR EVERYONE ELSE TODAY

- ☐ HOUSEKEEPER
- ☐ COMPLAINT DEPARTMENT
- ☐ SOCK FINDER
- ☐ THERAPIST
- ☐ CHAUFFEUR
- ☐ BOOBOO KISSER
- ☐ HOMEWORK TUTOR
- ☐ ALARM CLOCK
- ☐ TUSHY WIPER
- ☐ DOCTOR
- ☐ CHEF
- ☐ GOOD COP
- ☐ BAD COP
- ☐ STORYTELLER
- ☐ HUMAN HANKY
- ☐ MEDIATOR
- ☐ ATM
- ☐ COACH
- ☐ TOOTH FAIRY
- ☐ ....
- ☐ ALL OF THE ABOVE

ONE THING I COULD POSSIBLY DO FOR MYSELF TODAY	✓
01	

"REMEMBER, MOTHER KNOWS BEST"

MOTHER'S LITTLE HELPER

TODAY'S DATE
/   /

TODAY'S STRESS LEVEL
1   2   3   4   5   11

	STUFF TO DO FOR EVERYONE ELSE	✓	ITEMS TO BUY FOR EVERYONE ELSE	✓
01				
02				
03				
04				
05				
06				
07				
08				
09				
10				
11				
12				
13				
14				

JOBS I MUST PERFORM FOR EVERYONE ELSE TODAY

☐ HOUSEKEEPER ☐ ALARM CLOCK ☐ HUMAN HANKY
☐ COMPLAINT DEPARTMENT ☐ TUSHY WIPER ☐ MEDIATOR
☐ SOCK FINDER ☐ DOCTOR ☐ ATM
☐ THERAPIST ☐ CHEF ☐ COACH
☐ CHAUFFEUR ☐ GOOD COP ☐ TOOTH FAIRY
☐ BOOBOO KISSER ☐ BAD COP ☐ ....
☐ HOMEWORK TUTOR ☐ STORYTELLER ☐ ALL OF THE ABOVE

ONE THING I COULD POSSIBLY DO FOR MYSELF TODAY	✓
01	

"REMEMBER, MOTHER KNOWS BEST"

MOTHER'S LITTLE HELPER

TODAY'S DATE
/ /

TODAY'S STRESS LEVEL
1   2   3   4   5   11

	STUFF TO DO FOR EVERYONE ELSE	✓	ITEMS TO BUY FOR EVERYONE ELSE	✓
01				
02				
03				
04				
05				
06				
07				
08				
09				
10				
11				
12				
13				
14				

JOBS I MUST PERFORM FOR EVERYONE ELSE TODAY

☐ HOUSEKEEPER
☐ COMPLAINT DEPARTMENT
☐ SOCK FINDER
☐ THERAPIST
☐ CHAUFFEUR
☐ BOOBOO KISSER
☐ HOMEWORK TUTOR

☐ ALARM CLOCK
☐ TUSHY WIPER
☐ DOCTOR
☐ CHEF
☐ GOOD COP
☐ BAD COP
☐ STORYTELLER

☐ HUMAN HANKY
☐ MEDIATOR
☐ ATM
☐ COACH
☐ TOOTH FAIRY
☐ ....
☐ ALL OF THE ABOVE

ONE THING I COULD POSSIBLY DO FOR MYSELF TODAY	✓
01	

"REMEMBER, MOTHER KNOWS BEST"

MOTHER'S LITTLE HELPER

TODAY'S DATE

/ /

TODAY'S STRESS LEVEL

1 2 3 4 5 11

	STUFF TO DO FOR EVERYONE ELSE	✓	ITEMS TO BUY FOR EVERYONE ELSE	✓
01				
02				
03				
04				
05				
06				
07				
08				
09				
10				
11				
12				
13				
14				

JOBS I MUST PERFORM FOR EVERYONE ELSE TODAY

- ☐ HOUSEKEEPER
- ☐ COMPLAINT DEPARTMENT
- ☐ SOCK FINDER
- ☐ THERAPIST
- ☐ CHAUFFEUR
- ☐ BOOBOO KISSER
- ☐ HOMEWORK TUTOR
- ☐ ALARM CLOCK
- ☐ TUSHY WIPER
- ☐ DOCTOR
- ☐ CHEF
- ☐ GOOD COP
- ☐ BAD COP
- ☐ STORYTELLER
- ☐ HUMAN HANKY
- ☐ MEDIATOR
- ☐ ATM
- ☐ COACH
- ☐ TOOTH FAIRY
- ☐ ....
- ☐ ALL OF THE ABOVE

ONE THING I COULD POSSIBLY DO FOR MYSELF TODAY	✓
01	

"REMEMBER, MOTHER KNOWS BEST"

KNOCKKNOCKSTUFF.COM • © 2018 KNOCK KNOCK LLC

MOTHER'S LITTLE HELPER

	STUFF TO DO FOR EVERYONE ELSE	✓	ITEMS TO BUY FOR EVERYONE ELSE	✓
01				
02				
03				
04				
05				
06				
07				
08				
09				
10				
11				
12				
13				
14				

JOBS I MUST PERFORM FOR EVERYONE ELSE TODAY

☐ HOUSEKEEPER	☐ ALARM CLOCK	☐ HUMAN HANKY
☐ COMPLAINT DEPARTMENT	☐ TUSHY WIPER	☐ MEDIATOR
☐ SOCK FINDER	☐ DOCTOR	☐ ATM
☐ THERAPIST	☐ CHEF	☐ COACH
☐ CHAUFFEUR	☐ GOOD COP	☐ TOOTH FAIRY
☐ BOOBOO KISSER	☐ BAD COP	☐ ....
☐ HOMEWORK TUTOR	☐ STORYTELLER	☐ ALL OF THE ABOVE

ONE THING I COULD POSSIBLY DO FOR MYSELF TODAY ✓

01	

"REMEMBER, MOTHER KNOWS BEST"

MOTHER'S LITTLE HELPER

	STUFF TO DO FOR EVERYONE ELSE	✓	ITEMS TO BUY FOR EVERYONE ELSE	✓
01				
02				
03				
04				
05				
06				
07				
08				
09				
10				
11				
12				
13				
14				

JOBS I MUST PERFORM FOR EVERYONE ELSE TODAY

☐ HOUSEKEEPER
☐ COMPLAINT DEPARTMENT
☐ SOCK FINDER
☐ THERAPIST
☐ CHAUFFEUR
☐ BOOBOO KISSER
☐ HOMEWORK TUTOR

☐ ALARM CLOCK
☐ TUSHY WIPER
☐ DOCTOR
☐ CHEF
☐ GOOD COP
☐ BAD COP
☐ STORYTELLER

☐ HUMAN HANKY
☐ MEDIATOR
☐ ATM
☐ COACH
☐ TOOTH FAIRY
☐ ....
☐ ALL OF THE ABOVE

	ONE THING I COULD POSSIBLY DO FOR MYSELF TODAY	✓
01		

"REMEMBER, MOTHER KNOWS BEST"

MOTHER'S LITTLE HELPER

TODAY'S DATE
_____ / _____ / _____

TODAY'S STRESS LEVEL
1   2   3   4   5   11

	STUFF TO DO FOR EVERYONE ELSE	✓	ITEMS TO BUY FOR EVERYONE ELSE	✓
01				
02				
03				
04				
05				
06				
07				
08				
09				
10				
11				
12				
13				
14				

JOBS I MUST PERFORM FOR EVERYONE ELSE TODAY

☐ HOUSEKEEPER ☐ ALARM CLOCK ☐ HUMAN HANKY
☐ COMPLAINT DEPARTMENT ☐ TUSHY WIPER ☐ MEDIATOR
☐ SOCK FINDER ☐ DOCTOR ☐ ATM
☐ THERAPIST ☐ CHEF ☐ COACH
☐ CHAUFFEUR ☐ GOOD COP ☐ TOOTH FAIRY
☐ BOOBOO KISSER ☐ BAD COP ☐ ....
☐ HOMEWORK TUTOR ☐ STORYTELLER ☐ ALL OF THE ABOVE

ONE THING I COULD POSSIBLY DO FOR MYSELF TODAY	✓
01	

"REMEMBER, MOTHER KNOWS BEST"

MOTHER'S LITTLE HELPER

TODAY'S STRESS LEVEL

1   2   3   4   5   11

	STUFF TO DO FOR EVERYONE ELSE	✓	ITEMS TO BUY FOR EVERYONE ELSE	✓
01				
02				
03				
04				
05				
06				
07				
08				
09				
10				
11				
12				
13				
14				

JOBS I MUST PERFORM FOR EVERYONE ELSE TODAY

☐ HOUSEKEEPER   ☐ ALARM CLOCK   ☐ HUMAN HANKY
☐ COMPLAINT DEPARTMENT ☐ TUSHY WIPER   ☐ MEDIATOR
☐ SOCK FINDER   ☐ DOCTOR   ☐ ATM
☐ THERAPIST   ☐ CHEF   ☐ COACH
☐ CHAUFFEUR   ☐ GOOD COP   ☐ TOOTH FAIRY
☐ BOOBOO KISSER   ☐ BAD COP   ☐ ....
☐ HOMEWORK TUTOR   ☐ STORYTELLER   ☐ ALL OF THE ABOVE

	ONE THING I COULD POSSIBLY DO FOR MYSELF TODAY	✓
01		

"REMEMBER, MOTHER KNOWS BEST"

MOTHER'S
LITTLE HELPER

TODAY'S DATE

/ /

TODAY'S STRESS LEVEL

| 1 | 2 | 3 | 4 | 5 | 11 |

#	STUFF TO DO FOR EVERYONE ELSE	✓	ITEMS TO BUY FOR EVERYONE ELSE	✓
01				
02				
03				
04				
05				
06				
07				
08				
09				
10				
11				
12				
13				
14				

JOBS I MUST PERFORM FOR EVERYONE ELSE TODAY

- ☐ HOUSEKEEPER
- ☐ COMPLAINT DEPARTMENT
- ☐ SOCK FINDER
- ☐ THERAPIST
- ☐ CHAUFFEUR
- ☐ BOOBOO KISSER
- ☐ HOMEWORK TUTOR

- ☐ ALARM CLOCK
- ☐ TUSHY WIPER
- ☐ DOCTOR
- ☐ CHEF
- ☐ GOOD COP
- ☐ BAD COP
- ☐ STORYTELLER

- ☐ HUMAN HANKY
- ☐ MEDIATOR
- ☐ ATM
- ☐ COACH
- ☐ TOOTH FAIRY
- ☐ ....
- ☐ ALL OF THE ABOVE

ONE THING I COULD POSSIBLY DO FOR MYSELF TODAY ✓

01	

"REMEMBER, MOTHER KNOWS BEST"

MOTHER'S LITTLE HELPER

TODAY'S DATE
/   /

TODAY'S STRESS LEVEL
1   2   3   4   5   11

	STUFF TO DO FOR EVERYONE ELSE	✓	ITEMS TO BUY FOR EVERYONE ELSE	✓
01				
02				
03				
04				
05				
06				
07				
08				
09				
10				
11				
12				
13				
14				

JOBS I MUST PERFORM FOR EVERYONE ELSE TODAY

☐ HOUSEKEEPER   ☐ ALARM CLOCK   ☐ HUMAN HANKY

☐ COMPLAINT DEPARTMENT   ☐ TUSHY WIPER   ☐ MEDIATOR

☐ SOCK FINDER   ☐ DOCTOR   ☐ ATM

☐ THERAPIST   ☐ CHEF   ☐ COACH

☐ CHAUFFEUR   ☐ GOOD COP   ☐ TOOTH FAIRY

☐ BOOBOO KISSER   ☐ BAD COP   ☐ ....

☐ HOMEWORK TUTOR   ☐ STORYTELLER   ☐ ALL OF THE ABOVE

ONE THING I COULD POSSIBLY DO FOR MYSELF TODAY | ✓

01	

"REMEMBER, MOTHER KNOWS BEST"

MOTHER'S LITTLE HELPER

TODAY'S DATE

/ /

TODAY'S STRESS LEVEL

1 2 3 4 5 11

	STUFF TO DO FOR EVERYONE ELSE	✓	ITEMS TO BUY FOR EVERYONE ELSE	✓
01				
02				
03				
04				
05				
06				
07				
08				
09				
10				
11				
12				
13				
14				

JOBS I MUST PERFORM FOR EVERYONE ELSE TODAY

☐ HOUSEKEEPER   ☐ ALARM CLOCK   ☐ HUMAN HANKY

☐ COMPLAINT DEPARTMENT   ☐ TUSHY WIPER   ☐ MEDIATOR

☐ SOCK FINDER   ☐ DOCTOR   ☐ ATM

☐ THERAPIST   ☐ CHEF   ☐ COACH

☐ CHAUFFEUR   ☐ GOOD COP   ☐ TOOTH FAIRY

☐ BOOBOO KISSER   ☐ BAD COP   ☐ ....

☐ HOMEWORK TUTOR   ☐ STORYTELLER   ☐ ALL OF THE ABOVE

ONE THING I COULD POSSIBLY DO FOR MYSELF TODAY   ✓

01	

"REMEMBER, MOTHER KNOWS BEST"

MOTHER'S LITTLE HELPER

TODAY'S DATE
/ /

TODAY'S STRESS LEVEL
1 2 3 4 5 11

	STUFF TO DO FOR EVERYONE ELSE	✓	ITEMS TO BUY FOR EVERYONE ELSE	✓
01				
02				
03				
04				
05				
06				
07				
08				
09				
10				
11				
12				
13				
14				

JOBS I MUST PERFORM FOR EVERYONE ELSE TODAY

☐ HOUSEKEEPER   ☐ ALARM CLOCK   ☐ HUMAN HANKY
☐ COMPLAINT DEPARTMENT   ☐ TUSHY WIPER   ☐ MEDIATOR
☐ SOCK FINDER   ☐ DOCTOR   ☐ ATM
☐ THERAPIST   ☐ CHEF   ☐ COACH
☐ CHAUFFEUR   ☐ GOOD COP   ☐ TOOTH FAIRY
☐ BOOBOO KISSER   ☐ BAD COP   ☐ ....
☐ HOMEWORK TUTOR   ☐ STORYTELLER   ☐ ALL OF THE ABOVE

	ONE THING I COULD POSSIBLY DO FOR MYSELF TODAY	✓
01		

"REMEMBER, MOTHER KNOWS BEST"

MOTHER'S LITTLE HELPER

TODAY'S DATE

/ /

TODAY'S STRESS LEVEL

1 2 3 4 5 11

	STUFF TO DO FOR EVERYONE ELSE	✓	ITEMS TO BUY FOR EVERYONE ELSE	✓
01				
02				
03				
04				
05				
06				
07				
08				
09				
10				
11				
12				
13				
14				

JOBS I MUST PERFORM FOR EVERYONE ELSE TODAY

- ☐ HOUSEKEEPER
- ☐ COMPLAINT DEPARTMENT
- ☐ SOCK FINDER
- ☐ THERAPIST
- ☐ CHAUFFEUR
- ☐ BOOBOO KISSER
- ☐ HOMEWORK TUTOR

- ☐ ALARM CLOCK
- ☐ TUSHY WIPER
- ☐ DOCTOR
- ☐ CHEF
- ☐ GOOD COP
- ☐ BAD COP
- ☐ STORYTELLER

- ☐ HUMAN HANKY
- ☐ MEDIATOR
- ☐ ATM
- ☐ COACH
- ☐ TOOTH FAIRY
- ☐ ....
- ☐ ALL OF THE ABOVE

ONE THING I COULD POSSIBLY DO FOR MYSELF TODAY   ✓

01	

"REMEMBER, MOTHER KNOWS BEST"

MOTHER'S LITTLE HELPER

TODAY'S DATE
/ /

TODAY'S STRESS LEVEL
1 2 3 4 5 11

	STUFF TO DO FOR EVERYONE ELSE	✓	ITEMS TO BUY FOR EVERYONE ELSE	✓
01				
02				
03				
04				
05				
06				
07				
08				
09				
10				
11				
12				
13				
14				

JOBS I MUST PERFORM FOR EVERYONE ELSE TODAY

- ☐ HOUSEKEEPER
- ☐ COMPLAINT DEPARTMENT
- ☐ SOCK FINDER
- ☐ THERAPIST
- ☐ CHAUFFEUR
- ☐ BOOBOO KISSER
- ☐ HOMEWORK TUTOR

- ☐ ALARM CLOCK
- ☐ TUSHY WIPER
- ☐ DOCTOR
- ☐ CHEF
- ☐ GOOD COP
- ☐ BAD COP
- ☐ STORYTELLER

- ☐ HUMAN HANKY
- ☐ MEDIATOR
- ☐ ATM
- ☐ COACH
- ☐ TOOTH FAIRY
- ☐ ....
- ☐ ALL OF THE ABOVE

	ONE THING I COULD POSSIBLY DO FOR MYSELF TODAY	✓
01		

"REMEMBER, MOTHER KNOWS BEST"

MOTHER'S LITTLE HELPER

TODAY'S DATE
/ /

TODAY'S STRESS LEVEL
1   2   3   4   5   11

	STUFF TO DO FOR EVERYONE ELSE	✓	ITEMS TO BUY FOR EVERYONE ELSE	✓
01				
02				
03				
04				
05				
06				
07				
08				
09				
10				
11				
12				
13				
14				

JOBS I MUST PERFORM FOR EVERYONE ELSE TODAY

- ☐ HOUSEKEEPER
- ☐ COMPLAINT DEPARTMENT
- ☐ SOCK FINDER
- ☐ THERAPIST
- ☐ CHAUFFEUR
- ☐ BOOBOO KISSER
- ☐ HOMEWORK TUTOR
- ☐ ALARM CLOCK
- ☐ TUSHY WIPER
- ☐ DOCTOR
- ☐ CHEF
- ☐ GOOD COP
- ☐ BAD COP
- ☐ STORYTELLER
- ☐ HUMAN HANKY
- ☐ MEDIATOR
- ☐ ATM
- ☐ COACH
- ☐ TOOTH FAIRY
- ☐ ....
- ☐ ALL OF THE ABOVE

ONE THING I COULD POSSIBLY DO FOR MYSELF TODAY	✓
01	

"REMEMBER, MOTHER KNOWS BEST"

MOTHER'S LITTLE HELPER

TODAY'S DATE
/ /

TODAY'S STRESS LEVEL
1 2 3 4 5 11

	STUFF TO DO FOR EVERYONE ELSE	✓	ITEMS TO BUY FOR EVERYONE ELSE	✓
01				
02				
03				
04				
05				
06				
07				
08				
09				
10				
11				
12				
13				
14				

JOBS I MUST PERFORM FOR EVERYONE ELSE TODAY

- ☐ HOUSEKEEPER
- ☐ COMPLAINT DEPARTMENT
- ☐ SOCK FINDER
- ☐ THERAPIST
- ☐ CHAUFFEUR
- ☐ BOOBOO KISSER
- ☐ HOMEWORK TUTOR
- ☐ ALARM CLOCK
- ☐ TUSHY WIPER
- ☐ DOCTOR
- ☐ CHEF
- ☐ GOOD COP
- ☐ BAD COP
- ☐ STORYTELLER
- ☐ HUMAN HANKY
- ☐ MEDIATOR
- ☐ ATM
- ☐ COACH
- ☐ TOOTH FAIRY
- ☐ ....
- ☐ ALL OF THE ABOVE

ONE THING I COULD POSSIBLY DO FOR MYSELF TODAY

01		✓

"REMEMBER, MOTHER KNOWS BEST"

KNOCKKNOCKSTUFF.COM ■ © 2018 KNOCK KNOCK LLC

MOTHER'S LITTLE HELPER

TODAY'S DATE

/ /

TODAY'S STRESS LEVEL

1 2 3 4 5 11

	STUFF TO DO FOR EVERYONE ELSE	✓	ITEMS TO BUY FOR EVERYONE ELSE	✓
01				
02				
03				
04				
05				
06				
07				
08				
09				
10				
11				
12				
13				
14				

JOBS I MUST PERFORM FOR EVERYONE ELSE TODAY

- ☐ HOUSEKEEPER
- ☐ COMPLAINT DEPARTMENT
- ☐ SOCK FINDER
- ☐ THERAPIST
- ☐ CHAUFFEUR
- ☐ BOOBOO KISSER
- ☐ HOMEWORK TUTOR
- ☐ ALARM CLOCK
- ☐ TUSHY WIPER
- ☐ DOCTOR
- ☐ CHEF
- ☐ GOOD COP
- ☐ BAD COP
- ☐ STORYTELLER
- ☐ HUMAN HANKY
- ☐ MEDIATOR
- ☐ ATM
- ☐ COACH
- ☐ TOOTH FAIRY
- ☐ ....
- ☐ ALL OF THE ABOVE

	ONE THING I COULD POSSIBLY DO FOR MYSELF TODAY	✓
01		

"REMEMBER, MOTHER KNOWS BEST"

MOTHER'S LITTLE HELPER

TODAY'S DATE

/ /

TODAY'S STRESS LEVEL

1 2 3 4 5 11

	STUFF TO DO FOR EVERYONE ELSE	✓	ITEMS TO BUY FOR EVERYONE ELSE	✓
01				
02				
03				
04				
05				
06				
07				
08				
09				
10				
11				
12				
13				
14				

JOBS I MUST PERFORM FOR EVERYONE ELSE TODAY

☐ HOUSEKEEPER
☐ COMPLAINT DEPARTMENT
☐ SOCK FINDER
☐ THERAPIST
☐ CHAUFFEUR
☐ BOOBOO KISSER
☐ HOMEWORK TUTOR

☐ ALARM CLOCK
☐ TUSHY WIPER
☐ DOCTOR
☐ CHEF
☐ GOOD COP
☐ BAD COP
☐ STORYTELLER

☐ HUMAN HANKY
☐ MEDIATOR
☐ ATM
☐ COACH
☐ TOOTH FAIRY
☐ ....
☐ ALL OF THE ABOVE

ONE THING I COULD POSSIBLY DO FOR MYSELF TODAY	✓
01	

"REMEMBER, MOTHER KNOWS BEST"

MOTHER'S
LITTLE HELPER

TODAY'S STRESS LEVEL

| 1 | 2 | 3 | 4 | 5 | 11 |

	STUFF TO DO FOR EVERYONE ELSE	✓	ITEMS TO BUY FOR EVERYONE ELSE	✓
01				
02				
03				
04				
05				
06				
07				
08				
09				
10				
11				
12				
13				
14				

JOBS I MUST PERFORM FOR EVERYONE ELSE TODAY

- ☐ HOUSEKEEPER
- ☐ COMPLAINT DEPARTMENT
- ☐ SOCK FINDER
- ☐ THERAPIST
- ☐ CHAUFFEUR
- ☐ BOOBOO KISSER
- ☐ HOMEWORK TUTOR
- ☐ ALARM CLOCK
- ☐ TUSHY WIPER
- ☐ DOCTOR
- ☐ CHEF
- ☐ GOOD COP
- ☐ BAD COP
- ☐ STORYTELLER
- ☐ HUMAN HANKY
- ☐ MEDIATOR
- ☐ ATM
- ☐ COACH
- ☐ TOOTH FAIRY
- ☐ ....
- ☐ ALL OF THE ABOVE

ONE THING I COULD POSSIBLY DO FOR MYSELF TODAY	✓
01	

"REMEMBER, MOTHER KNOWS BEST"

MOTHER'S LITTLE HELPER

TODAY'S DATE
/   /

TODAY'S STRESS LEVEL

1   2   3   4   5   11

	STUFF TO DO FOR EVERYONE ELSE	✓	ITEMS TO BUY FOR EVERYONE ELSE	✓
01				
02				
03				
04				
05				
06				
07				
08				
09				
10				
11				
12				
13				
14				

JOBS I MUST PERFORM FOR EVERYONE ELSE TODAY

☐ HOUSEKEEPER	☐ ALARM CLOCK	☐ HUMAN HANKY
☐ COMPLAINT DEPARTMENT	☐ TUSHY WIPER	☐ MEDIATOR
☐ SOCK FINDER	☐ DOCTOR	☐ ATM
☐ THERAPIST	☐ CHEF	☐ COACH
☐ CHAUFFEUR	☐ GOOD COP	☐ TOOTH FAIRY
☐ BOOBOO KISSER	☐ BAD COP	☐ ....
☐ HOMEWORK TUTOR	☐ STORYTELLER	☐ ALL OF THE ABOVE

ONE THING I COULD POSSIBLY DO FOR MYSELF TODAY	✓
01	

"REMEMBER, MOTHER KNOWS BEST"

MOTHER'S
LITTLE HELPER

TODAY'S DATE

/ /

TODAY'S STRESS LEVEL

1   2   3   4   5   11

	STUFF TO DO FOR EVERYONE ELSE	✓	ITEMS TO BUY FOR EVERYONE ELSE	✓
01				
02				
03				
04				
05				
06				
07				
08				
09				
10				
11				
12				
13				
14				

JOBS I MUST PERFORM FOR EVERYONE ELSE TODAY

☐ HOUSEKEEPER
☐ COMPLAINT DEPARTMENT
☐ SOCK FINDER
☐ THERAPIST
☐ CHAUFFEUR
☐ BOOBOO KISSER
☐ HOMEWORK TUTOR

☐ ALARM CLOCK
☐ TUSHY WIPER
☐ DOCTOR
☐ CHEF
☐ GOOD COP
☐ BAD COP
☐ STORYTELLER

☐ HUMAN HANKY
☐ MEDIATOR
☐ ATM
☐ COACH
☐ TOOTH FAIRY
☐ ....
☐ ALL OF THE ABOVE

	ONE THING I COULD POSSIBLY DO FOR MYSELF TODAY	✓
01		

"REMEMBER, MOTHER KNOWS BEST"

MOTHER'S LITTLE HELPER

TODAY'S DATE

/ /

TODAY'S STRESS LEVEL

1   2   3   4   5   11

	STUFF TO DO FOR EVERYONE ELSE	✓	ITEMS TO BUY FOR EVERYONE ELSE	✓
01				
02				
03				
04				
05				
06				
07				
08				
09				
10				
11				
12				
13				
14				

JOBS I MUST PERFORM FOR EVERYONE ELSE TODAY

- ☐ HOUSEKEEPER
- ☐ COMPLAINT DEPARTMENT
- ☐ SOCK FINDER
- ☐ THERAPIST
- ☐ CHAUFFEUR
- ☐ BOOBOO KISSER
- ☐ HOMEWORK TUTOR

- ☐ ALARM CLOCK
- ☐ TUSHY WIPER
- ☐ DOCTOR
- ☐ CHEF
- ☐ GOOD COP
- ☐ BAD COP
- ☐ STORYTELLER

- ☐ HUMAN HANKY
- ☐ MEDIATOR
- ☐ ATM
- ☐ COACH
- ☐ TOOTH FAIRY
- ☐ ....
- ☐ ALL OF THE ABOVE

	ONE THING I COULD POSSIBLY DO FOR MYSELF TODAY	✓
01		

"REMEMBER, MOTHER KNOWS BEST"

MOTHER'S LITTLE HELPER

TODAY'S STRESS LEVEL

1   2   3   4   5   11

	STUFF TO DO FOR EVERYONE ELSE	✓	ITEMS TO BUY FOR EVERYONE ELSE	✓
01				
02				
03				
04				
05				
06				
07				
08				
09				
10				
11				
12				
13				
14				

JOBS I MUST PERFORM FOR EVERYONE ELSE TODAY

- ☐ HOUSEKEEPER
- ☐ COMPLAINT DEPARTMENT
- ☐ SOCK FINDER
- ☐ THERAPIST
- ☐ CHAUFFEUR
- ☐ BOOBOO KISSER
- ☐ HOMEWORK TUTOR
- ☐ ALARM CLOCK
- ☐ TUSHY WIPER
- ☐ DOCTOR
- ☐ CHEF
- ☐ GOOD COP
- ☐ BAD COP
- ☐ STORYTELLER
- ☐ HUMAN HANKY
- ☐ MEDIATOR
- ☐ ATM
- ☐ COACH
- ☐ TOOTH FAIRY
- ☐ ....
- ☐ ALL OF THE ABOVE

	ONE THING I COULD POSSIBLY DO FOR MYSELF TODAY	✓
01		

"REMEMBER, MOTHER KNOWS BEST"

MOTHER'S LITTLE HELPER

	STUFF TO DO FOR EVERYONE ELSE	✓	ITEMS TO BUY FOR EVERYONE ELSE	✓
01				
02				
03				
04				
05				
06				
07				
08				
09				
10				
11				
12				
13				
14				

JOBS I MUST PERFORM FOR EVERYONE ELSE TODAY

☐ HOUSEKEEPER	☐ ALARM CLOCK	☐ HUMAN HANKY
☐ COMPLAINT DEPARTMENT	☐ TUSHY WIPER	☐ MEDIATOR
☐ SOCK FINDER	☐ DOCTOR	☐ ATM
☐ THERAPIST	☐ CHEF	☐ COACH
☐ CHAUFFEUR	☐ GOOD COP	☐ TOOTH FAIRY
☐ BOOBOO KISSER	☐ BAD COP	☐ ....
☐ HOMEWORK TUTOR	☐ STORYTELLER	☐ ALL OF THE ABOVE

ONE THING I COULD POSSIBLY DO FOR MYSELF TODAY	✓
01	

"REMEMBER, MOTHER KNOWS BEST"

MOTHER'S
LITTLE HELPER

TODAY'S DATE

/ /

TODAY'S STRESS LEVEL

1 2 3 4 5 11

	STUFF TO DO FOR EVERYONE ELSE	✓	ITEMS TO BUY FOR EVERYONE ELSE	✓
01				
02				
03				
04				
05				
06				
07				
08				
09				
10				
11				
12				
13				
14				

JOBS I MUST PERFORM FOR EVERYONE ELSE TODAY

- ☐ HOUSEKEEPER
- ☐ COMPLAINT DEPARTMENT
- ☐ SOCK FINDER
- ☐ THERAPIST
- ☐ CHAUFFEUR
- ☐ BOOBOO KISSER
- ☐ HOMEWORK TUTOR

- ☐ ALARM CLOCK
- ☐ TUSHY WIPER
- ☐ DOCTOR
- ☐ CHEF
- ☐ GOOD COP
- ☐ BAD COP
- ☐ STORYTELLER

- ☐ HUMAN HANKY
- ☐ MEDIATOR
- ☐ ATM
- ☐ COACH
- ☐ TOOTH FAIRY
- ☐ ....
- ☐ ALL OF THE ABOVE

	ONE THING I COULD POSSIBLY DO FOR MYSELF TODAY	✓
01		

"REMEMBER, MOTHER KNOWS BEST"

MOTHER'S LITTLE HELPER

	STUFF TO DO FOR EVERYONE ELSE	✓	ITEMS TO BUY FOR EVERYONE ELSE	✓
01				
02				
03				
04				
05				
06				
07				
08				
09				
10				
11				
12				
13				
14				

JOBS I MUST PERFORM FOR EVERYONE ELSE TODAY

- ☐ HOUSEKEEPER
- ☐ COMPLAINT DEPARTMENT
- ☐ SOCK FINDER
- ☐ THERAPIST
- ☐ CHAUFFEUR
- ☐ BOOBOO KISSER
- ☐ HOMEWORK TUTOR

- ☐ ALARM CLOCK
- ☐ TUSHY WIPER
- ☐ DOCTOR
- ☐ CHEF
- ☐ GOOD COP
- ☐ BAD COP
- ☐ STORYTELLER

- ☐ HUMAN HANKY
- ☐ MEDIATOR
- ☐ ATM
- ☐ COACH
- ☐ TOOTH FAIRY
- ☐ ....
- ☐ ALL OF THE ABOVE

	ONE THING I COULD POSSIBLY DO FOR MYSELF TODAY	✓
01		

"REMEMBER, MOTHER KNOWS BEST"

MOTHER'S LITTLE HELPER

TODAY'S DATE

/ /

TODAY'S STRESS LEVEL

1 2 3 4 5 11

	STUFF TO DO FOR EVERYONE ELSE	✓	ITEMS TO BUY FOR EVERYONE ELSE	✓
01				
02				
03				
04				
05				
06				
07				
08				
09				
10				
11				
12				
13				
14				

JOBS I MUST PERFORM FOR EVERYONE ELSE TODAY

☐ HOUSEKEEPER   ☐ ALARM CLOCK   ☐ HUMAN HANKY
☐ COMPLAINT DEPARTMENT ☐ TUSHY WIPER   ☐ MEDIATOR
☐ SOCK FINDER   ☐ DOCTOR   ☐ ATM
☐ THERAPIST   ☐ CHEF   ☐ COACH
☐ CHAUFFEUR   ☐ GOOD COP   ☐ TOOTH FAIRY
☐ BOOBOO KISSER   ☐ BAD COP   ☐ ....
☐ HOMEWORK TUTOR   ☐ STORYTELLER   ☐ ALL OF THE ABOVE

ONE THING I COULD POSSIBLY DO FOR MYSELF TODAY ✓

01	

"REMEMBER, MOTHER KNOWS BEST"

MOTHER'S LITTLE HELPER

TODAY'S DATE

/ /

TODAY'S STRESS LEVEL

1 2 3 4 5 11

	STUFF TO DO FOR EVERYONE ELSE	✓	ITEMS TO BUY FOR EVERYONE ELSE	✓
01				
02				
03				
04				
05				
06				
07				
08				
09				
10				
11				
12				
13				
14				

JOBS I MUST PERFORM FOR EVERYONE ELSE TODAY

☐ HOUSEKEEPER   ☐ ALARM CLOCK   ☐ HUMAN HANKY

☐ COMPLAINT DEPARTMENT   ☐ TUSHY WIPER   ☐ MEDIATOR

☐ SOCK FINDER   ☐ DOCTOR   ☐ ATM

☐ THERAPIST   ☐ CHEF   ☐ COACH

☐ CHAUFFEUR   ☐ GOOD COP   ☐ TOOTH FAIRY

☐ BOOBOO KISSER   ☐ BAD COP   ☐ ....

☐ HOMEWORK TUTOR   ☐ STORYTELLER   ☐ ALL OF THE ABOVE

ONE THING I COULD POSSIBLY DO FOR MYSELF TODAY   ✓

01	

"REMEMBER, MOTHER KNOWS BEST"

MOTHER'S LITTLE HELPER

	STUFF TO DO FOR EVERYONE ELSE	✓	ITEMS TO BUY FOR EVERYONE ELSE	✓
01				
02				
03				
04				
05				
06				
07				
08				
09				
10				
11				
12				
13				
14				

JOBS I MUST PERFORM FOR EVERYONE ELSE TODAY

- ☐ HOUSEKEEPER
- ☐ COMPLAINT DEPARTMENT
- ☐ SOCK FINDER
- ☐ THERAPIST
- ☐ CHAUFFEUR
- ☐ BOOBOO KISSER
- ☐ HOMEWORK TUTOR

- ☐ ALARM CLOCK
- ☐ TUSHY WIPER
- ☐ DOCTOR
- ☐ CHEF
- ☐ GOOD COP
- ☐ BAD COP
- ☐ STORYTELLER

- ☐ HUMAN HANKY
- ☐ MEDIATOR
- ☐ ATM
- ☐ COACH
- ☐ TOOTH FAIRY
- ☐ ....
- ☐ ALL OF THE ABOVE

	ONE THING I COULD POSSIBLY DO FOR MYSELF TODAY	✓
01		

"REMEMBER, MOTHER KNOWS BEST"

MOTHER'S LITTLE HELPER

	STUFF TO DO FOR EVERYONE ELSE	✓	ITEMS TO BUY FOR EVERYONE ELSE	✓
01				
02				
03				
04				
05				
06				
07				
08				
09				
10				
11				
12				
13				
14				

JOBS I MUST PERFORM FOR EVERYONE ELSE TODAY

- ☐ HOUSEKEEPER
- ☐ COMPLAINT DEPARTMENT
- ☐ SOCK FINDER
- ☐ THERAPIST
- ☐ CHAUFFEUR
- ☐ BOOBOO KISSER
- ☐ HOMEWORK TUTOR

- ☐ ALARM CLOCK
- ☐ TUSHY WIPER
- ☐ DOCTOR
- ☐ CHEF
- ☐ GOOD COP
- ☐ BAD COP
- ☐ STORYTELLER

- ☐ HUMAN HANKY
- ☐ MEDIATOR
- ☐ ATM
- ☐ COACH
- ☐ TOOTH FAIRY
- ☐ ....
- ☐ ALL OF THE ABOVE

	ONE THING I COULD POSSIBLY DO FOR MYSELF TODAY	✓
01		

"REMEMBER, MOTHER KNOWS BEST"

MOTHER'S LITTLE HELPER

	STUFF TO DO FOR EVERYONE ELSE	✓	ITEMS TO BUY FOR EVERYONE ELSE	✓
01				
02				
03				
04				
05				
06				
07				
08				
09				
10				
11				
12				
13				
14				

JOBS I MUST PERFORM FOR EVERYONE ELSE TODAY

- ☐ HOUSEKEEPER
- ☐ COMPLAINT DEPARTMENT
- ☐ SOCK FINDER
- ☐ THERAPIST
- ☐ CHAUFFEUR
- ☐ BOOBOO KISSER
- ☐ HOMEWORK TUTOR

- ☐ ALARM CLOCK
- ☐ TUSHY WIPER
- ☐ DOCTOR
- ☐ CHEF
- ☐ GOOD COP
- ☐ BAD COP
- ☐ STORYTELLER

- ☐ HUMAN HANKY
- ☐ MEDIATOR
- ☐ ATM
- ☐ COACH
- ☐ TOOTH FAIRY
- ☐ ....
- ☐ ALL OF THE ABOVE

	ONE THING I COULD POSSIBLY DO FOR MYSELF TODAY	✓
01		

"REMEMBER, MOTHER KNOWS BEST"

MOTHER'S LITTLE HELPER

	STUFF TO DO FOR EVERYONE ELSE	✓	ITEMS TO BUY FOR EVERYONE ELSE	✓
01				
02				
03				
04				
05				
06				
07				
08				
09				
10				
11				
12				
13				
14				

JOBS I MUST PERFORM FOR EVERYONE ELSE TODAY

- ☐ HOUSEKEEPER
- ☐ COMPLAINT DEPARTMENT
- ☐ SOCK FINDER
- ☐ THERAPIST
- ☐ CHAUFFEUR
- ☐ BOOBOO KISSER
- ☐ HOMEWORK TUTOR

- ☐ ALARM CLOCK
- ☐ TUSHY WIPER
- ☐ DOCTOR
- ☐ CHEF
- ☐ GOOD COP
- ☐ BAD COP
- ☐ STORYTELLER

- ☐ HUMAN HANKY
- ☐ MEDIATOR
- ☐ ATM
- ☐ COACH
- ☐ TOOTH FAIRY
- ☐ ....
- ☐ ALL OF THE ABOVE

ONE THING I COULD POSSIBLY DO FOR MYSELF TODAY	✓
01	

"REMEMBER, MOTHER KNOWS BEST"

MOTHER'S LITTLE HELPER

	STUFF TO DO FOR EVERYONE ELSE	✓	ITEMS TO BUY FOR EVERYONE ELSE	✓
01				
02				
03				
04				
05				
06				
07				
08				
09				
10				
11				
12				
13				
14				

JOBS I MUST PERFORM FOR EVERYONE ELSE TODAY

- ☐ HOUSEKEEPER
- ☐ COMPLAINT DEPARTMENT
- ☐ SOCK FINDER
- ☐ THERAPIST
- ☐ CHAUFFEUR
- ☐ BOOBOO KISSER
- ☐ HOMEWORK TUTOR
- ☐ ALARM CLOCK
- ☐ TUSHY WIPER
- ☐ DOCTOR
- ☐ CHEF
- ☐ GOOD COP
- ☐ BAD COP
- ☐ STORYTELLER
- ☐ HUMAN HANKY
- ☐ MEDIATOR
- ☐ ATM
- ☐ COACH
- ☐ TOOTH FAIRY
- ☐ ....
- ☐ ALL OF THE ABOVE

ONE THING I COULD POSSIBLY DO FOR MYSELF TODAY	✓
01	

"REMEMBER, MOTHER KNOWS BEST"

MOTHER'S
LITTLE HELPER

	STUFF TO DO FOR EVERYONE ELSE	✓	ITEMS TO BUY FOR EVERYONE ELSE	✓
01				
02				
03				
04				
05				
06				
07				
08				
09				
10				
11				
12				
13				
14				

JOBS I MUST PERFORM FOR EVERYONE ELSE TODAY

☐ HOUSEKEEPER	☐ ALARM CLOCK	☐ HUMAN HANKY
☐ COMPLAINT DEPARTMENT	☐ TUSHY WIPER	☐ MEDIATOR
☐ SOCK FINDER	☐ DOCTOR	☐ ATM
☐ THERAPIST	☐ CHEF	☐ COACH
☐ CHAUFFEUR	☐ GOOD COP	☐ TOOTH FAIRY
☐ BOOBOO KISSER	☐ BAD COP	☐ ....
☐ HOMEWORK TUTOR	☐ STORYTELLER	☐ ALL OF THE ABOVE

	ONE THING I COULD POSSIBLY DO FOR MYSELF TODAY	✓
01		

"REMEMBER, MOTHER KNOWS BEST"

MOTHER'S LITTLE HELPER

TODAY'S DATE

/ /

TODAY'S STRESS LEVEL

1 2 3 4 5 11

	STUFF TO DO FOR EVERYONE ELSE	✓	ITEMS TO BUY FOR EVERYONE ELSE	✓
01				
02				
03				
04				
05				
06				
07				
08				
09				
10				
11				
12				
13				
14				

JOBS I MUST PERFORM FOR EVERYONE ELSE TODAY

- ☐ HOUSEKEEPER
- ☐ COMPLAINT DEPARTMENT
- ☐ SOCK FINDER
- ☐ THERAPIST
- ☐ CHAUFFEUR
- ☐ BOOBOO KISSER
- ☐ HOMEWORK TUTOR

- ☐ ALARM CLOCK
- ☐ TUSHY WIPER
- ☐ DOCTOR
- ☐ CHEF
- ☐ GOOD COP
- ☐ BAD COP
- ☐ STORYTELLER

- ☐ HUMAN HANKY
- ☐ MEDIATOR
- ☐ ATM
- ☐ COACH
- ☐ TOOTH FAIRY
- ☐ ....
- ☐ ALL OF THE ABOVE

	ONE THING I COULD POSSIBLY DO FOR MYSELF TODAY	✓
01		

"REMEMBER, MOTHER KNOWS BEST"

MOTHER'S LITTLE HELPER

	STUFF TO DO FOR EVERYONE ELSE	✓	ITEMS TO BUY FOR EVERYONE ELSE	✓
01				
02				
03				
04				
05				
06				
07				
08				
09				
10				
11				
12				
13				
14				

JOBS I MUST PERFORM FOR EVERYONE ELSE TODAY

- ☐ HOUSEKEEPER
- ☐ COMPLAINT DEPARTMENT
- ☐ SOCK FINDER
- ☐ THERAPIST
- ☐ CHAUFFEUR
- ☐ BOOBOO KISSER
- ☐ HOMEWORK TUTOR

- ☐ ALARM CLOCK
- ☐ TUSHY WIPER
- ☐ DOCTOR
- ☐ CHEF
- ☐ GOOD COP
- ☐ BAD COP
- ☐ STORYTELLER

- ☐ HUMAN HANKY
- ☐ MEDIATOR
- ☐ ATM
- ☐ COACH
- ☐ TOOTH FAIRY
- ☐ ....
- ☐ ALL OF THE ABOVE

ONE THING I COULD POSSIBLY DO FOR MYSELF TODAY	✓
01	

"REMEMBER, MOTHER KNOWS BEST"

MOTHER'S LITTLE HELPER

	STUFF TO DO FOR EVERYONE ELSE	✓	ITEMS TO BUY FOR EVERYONE ELSE	✓
01				
02				
03				
04				
05				
06				
07				
08				
09				
10				
11				
12				
13				
14				

JOBS I MUST PERFORM FOR EVERYONE ELSE TODAY

☐ HOUSEKEEPER	☐ ALARM CLOCK	☐ HUMAN HANKY
☐ COMPLAINT DEPARTMENT	☐ TUSHY WIPER	☐ MEDIATOR
☐ SOCK FINDER	☐ DOCTOR	☐ ATM
☐ THERAPIST	☐ CHEF	☐ COACH
☐ CHAUFFEUR	☐ GOOD COP	☐ TOOTH FAIRY
☐ BOOBOO KISSER	☐ BAD COP	☐ ....
☐ HOMEWORK TUTOR	☐ STORYTELLER	☐ ALL OF THE ABOVE

ONE THING I COULD POSSIBLY DO FOR MYSELF TODAY   ✓

01	

"REMEMBER, MOTHER KNOWS BEST"

MOTHER'S LITTLE HELPER

	STUFF TO DO FOR EVERYONE ELSE	✓	ITEMS TO BUY FOR EVERYONE ELSE	✓
01				
02				
03				
04				
05				
06				
07				
08				
09				
10				
11				
12				
13				
14				

JOBS I MUST PERFORM FOR EVERYONE ELSE TODAY

☐ HOUSEKEEPER	☐ ALARM CLOCK	☐ HUMAN HANKY
☐ COMPLAINT DEPARTMENT	☐ TUSHY WIPER	☐ MEDIATOR
☐ SOCK FINDER	☐ DOCTOR	☐ ATM
☐ THERAPIST	☐ CHEF	☐ COACH
☐ CHAUFFEUR	☐ GOOD COP	☐ TOOTH FAIRY
☐ BOOBOO KISSER	☐ BAD COP	☐ ....
☐ HOMEWORK TUTOR	☐ STORYTELLER	☐ ALL OF THE ABOVE

ONE THING I COULD POSSIBLY DO FOR MYSELF TODAY | ✓

01		

"REMEMBER, MOTHER KNOWS BEST"

MOTHER'S LITTLE HELPER

TODAY'S DATE

/ /

TODAY'S STRESS LEVEL

1   2   3   4   5   11

	STUFF TO DO FOR EVERYONE ELSE	✓	ITEMS TO BUY FOR EVERYONE ELSE	✓
01				
02				
03				
04				
05				
06				
07				
08				
09				
10				
11				
12				
13				
14				

JOBS I MUST PERFORM FOR EVERYONE ELSE TODAY

- ☐ HOUSEKEEPER
- ☐ COMPLAINT DEPARTMENT
- ☐ SOCK FINDER
- ☐ THERAPIST
- ☐ CHAUFFEUR
- ☐ BOOBOO KISSER
- ☐ HOMEWORK TUTOR

- ☐ ALARM CLOCK
- ☐ TUSHY WIPER
- ☐ DOCTOR
- ☐ CHEF
- ☐ GOOD COP
- ☐ BAD COP
- ☐ STORYTELLER

- ☐ HUMAN HANKY
- ☐ MEDIATOR
- ☐ ATM
- ☐ COACH
- ☐ TOOTH FAIRY
- ☐ ....
- ☐ ALL OF THE ABOVE

ONE THING I COULD POSSIBLY DO FOR MYSELF TODAY

		✓
01		

"REMEMBER, MOTHER KNOWS BEST"

MOTHER'S LITTLE HELPER

TODAY'S STRESS LEVEL

| 1 | 2 | 3 | 4 | 5 | 11 |

	STUFF TO DO FOR EVERYONE ELSE	✓	ITEMS TO BUY FOR EVERYONE ELSE	✓
01				
02				
03				
04				
05				
06				
07				
08				
09				
10				
11				
12				
13				
14				

JOBS I MUST PERFORM FOR EVERYONE ELSE TODAY

- ☐ HOUSEKEEPER
- ☐ COMPLAINT DEPARTMENT
- ☐ SOCK FINDER
- ☐ THERAPIST
- ☐ CHAUFFEUR
- ☐ BOOBOO KISSER
- ☐ HOMEWORK TUTOR

- ☐ ALARM CLOCK
- ☐ TUSHY WIPER
- ☐ DOCTOR
- ☐ CHEF
- ☐ GOOD COP
- ☐ BAD COP
- ☐ STORYTELLER

- ☐ HUMAN HANKY
- ☐ MEDIATOR
- ☐ ATM
- ☐ COACH
- ☐ TOOTH FAIRY
- ☐ ....
- ☐ ALL OF THE ABOVE

	ONE THING I COULD POSSIBLY DO FOR MYSELF TODAY	✓
01		

"REMEMBER, MOTHER KNOWS BEST"

MOTHER'S LITTLE HELPER

TODAY'S DATE

/   /

TODAY'S STRESS LEVEL

1   2   3   4   5   11

	STUFF TO DO FOR EVERYONE ELSE	✓	ITEMS TO BUY FOR EVERYONE ELSE	✓
01				
02				
03				
04				
05				
06				
07				
08				
09				
10				
11				
12				
13				
14				

JOBS I MUST PERFORM FOR EVERYONE ELSE TODAY

☐ HOUSEKEEPER ☐ ALARM CLOCK ☐ HUMAN HANKY
☐ COMPLAINT DEPARTMENT ☐ TUSHY WIPER ☐ MEDIATOR
☐ SOCK FINDER ☐ DOCTOR ☐ ATM
☐ THERAPIST ☐ CHEF ☐ COACH
☐ CHAUFFEUR ☐ GOOD COP ☐ TOOTH FAIRY
☐ BOOBOO KISSER ☐ BAD COP ☐ ....
☐ HOMEWORK TUTOR ☐ STORYTELLER ☐ ALL OF THE ABOVE

ONE THING I COULD POSSIBLY DO FOR MYSELF TODAY	✓
01	

"REMEMBER, MOTHER KNOWS BEST"

MOTHER'S
LITTLE HELPER

TODAY'S STRESS LEVEL

| 1 | 2 | 3 | 4 | 5 | 11 |

	STUFF TO DO FOR EVERYONE ELSE	✓	ITEMS TO BUY FOR EVERYONE ELSE	✓
01				
02				
03				
04				
05				
06				
07				
08				
09				
10				
11				
12				
13				
14				

JOBS I MUST PERFORM FOR EVERYONE ELSE TODAY

- ☐ HOUSEKEEPER
- ☐ COMPLAINT DEPARTMENT
- ☐ SOCK FINDER
- ☐ THERAPIST
- ☐ CHAUFFEUR
- ☐ BOOBOO KISSER
- ☐ HOMEWORK TUTOR

- ☐ ALARM CLOCK
- ☐ TUSHY WIPER
- ☐ DOCTOR
- ☐ CHEF
- ☐ GOOD COP
- ☐ BAD COP
- ☐ STORYTELLER

- ☐ HUMAN HANKY
- ☐ MEDIATOR
- ☐ ATM
- ☐ COACH
- ☐ TOOTH FAIRY
- ☐ ....
- ☐ ALL OF THE ABOVE

ONE THING I COULD POSSIBLY DO FOR MYSELF TODAY	✓
01	

"REMEMBER, MOTHER KNOWS BEST"

MOTHER'S LITTLE HELPER

TODAY'S DATE

/ /

TODAY'S STRESS LEVEL

1 2 3 4 5 11

	STUFF TO DO FOR EVERYONE ELSE	✓	ITEMS TO BUY FOR EVERYONE ELSE	✓
01				
02				
03				
04				
05				
06				
07				
08				
09				
10				
11				
12				
13				
14				

JOBS I MUST PERFORM FOR EVERYONE ELSE TODAY

☐ HOUSEKEEPER   ☐ ALARM CLOCK   ☐ HUMAN HANKY

☐ COMPLAINT DEPARTMENT   ☐ TUSHY WIPER   ☐ MEDIATOR

☐ SOCK FINDER   ☐ DOCTOR   ☐ ATM

☐ THERAPIST   ☐ CHEF   ☐ COACH

☐ CHAUFFEUR   ☐ GOOD COP   ☐ TOOTH FAIRY

☐ BOOBOO KISSER   ☐ BAD COP   ☐ ....

☐ HOMEWORK TUTOR   ☐ STORYTELLER   ☐ ALL OF THE ABOVE

ONE THING I COULD POSSIBLY DO FOR MYSELF TODAY

✓

01	

"REMEMBER, MOTHER KNOWS BEST"